Millie Marotta's

Curious
Creatures

First published in the United Kingdom in 2019 by
Batsford
43 Great Ormond Street
London
WC1N 3HZ
United Kingdom

An imprint of Pavilion Books Group Ltd

ISBN: 9781849946247

A CIP catalogue record for this book is available
from the British Library.

25 24 23 22 21 20
3

Repro by Mission Productions Ltd, Hong Kong
Printed in China

This book can be ordered direct from the publisher at the website:
www.pavilionbooks.com, or try your local bookshop.

Millie Marotta's

Curious
Creatures

pocket colouring

BATSFORD

Introduction

If you are familiar with any of my previous colouring books you will know that I am somewhat fascinated by the animal kingdom. From a very young age I was utterly captivated by the marvels of our natural world and I feel incredibly privileged that my work allows me to combine my love of drawing with my passion for wildlife.

With *Curious Creatures* being my fourth colouring book, I would like to say that the process of selecting which animals will be included becomes a little easier, but it really doesn't. There are just so many amazing creatures out there to choose from, each with its own unique characteristics and qualities – and this is where the idea for *Curious Creatures* came from. For this book I decided to bring together a collection of animals that I find quite remarkable, slightly peculiar, unusual, quirky or even a little strange. But all quite beautiful to me.

It was still very hard to narrow it down to those that eventually made the pages of the book, but in the end I settled on some of my favourites. From flamboyant show-offs to masters of camouflage, this book brings together a rich array of intriguing birds, fish, mammals, amphibians, reptiles and invertebrates for you to enjoy and colour to your heart's content. Some were chosen for their bizarre behaviour, others for their unusual physical appearance or even for their incredible survival skills. From the Amazonian royal flycatcher with its flamboyant feathered headdress to the magical flying fish. From the splendour of the lion's mane jellyfish to the downright bizarre yet utterly charming duck-billed platypus.

My illustrations always begin as quite realistic drawings of the creatures, keeping the form of the animal very much true to life. I then begin to elaborate, building up lots of detail by adding intricate patterns and ornate embellishments, resulting in a collection of real creatures with a creative twist. From time to time readers ask me about specific animals in previous books. With that in mind and given that some of the animals in *Curious Creatures* might be a little less obvious, I have decided to include a 'contents page', listing each animal in the order they appear, which you will find at the back of the book. While a great many of you like to let your imagination run wild when choosing your colours, there are others who like to create something that is more true to life, so I hope this list helps those of you who might want to research the animals a little before diving in with your colours.

What I love about creating these books is that not only do I get to bring together my two passions in life – nature and drawing – I also get to share the experience with you, the reader. Seeing my black-and-white line drawings brought to life with colour and watching how differently you each go about turning these images into something of your own is incredibly exciting and tremendously inspiring.

I am thrilled to see how colouring has been embraced across the world and has become a regular activity for so many people. I continue to be amazed by the colouring community and how enthusiastic, passionate and involved you are. On a daily basis I see what I can frankly only describe as ridiculously beautiful examples of coloured pages from my books being shared over social media – people are running clubs and competitions, providing online tutorials, sharing colouring tips and talking about materials and techniques. A whole community has come together over colouring and I think that is a wonderful thing.

Occasionally I'm asked how a particular image should be coloured, or which materials, colours or techniques should be used. My answer is always the same – there is no right or wrong way and there are no rules. Each one of you will colour in your own unique way. You will have your own thoughts and ideas about how you choose to work with the illustrations and it is this individual approach that makes these images ultimately become your own art works.

For those of you who enjoy adding your own drawings to the illustrations as well as colouring them, I have scattered a few images amongst the pages that are less detailed than most, leaving empty space for you to add your own drawn details, textures and patterns. I have also included some blank pages at the back of the book, which you might like to use for drawing your own curious creatures or for testing out new colours and materials.

However you like to colour, whatever materials you choose to use and whatever techniques you like to explore, I really hope you enjoy the illustrations in this book. I can't wait to see how differently each of you will flood these pages with colour, bringing to life your very own vibrant world of curious creatures.

Millie Marotta

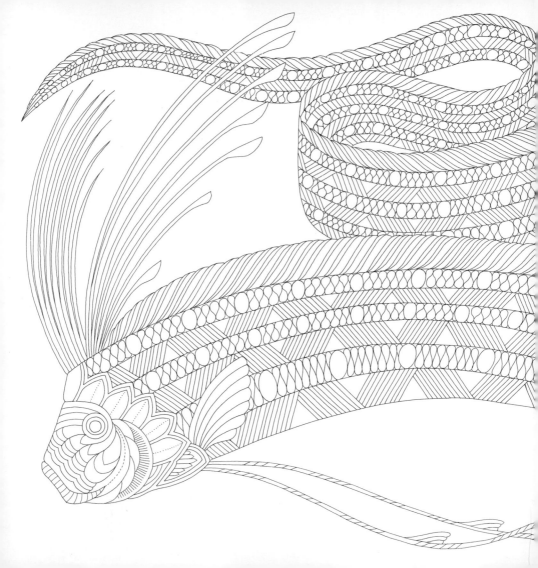

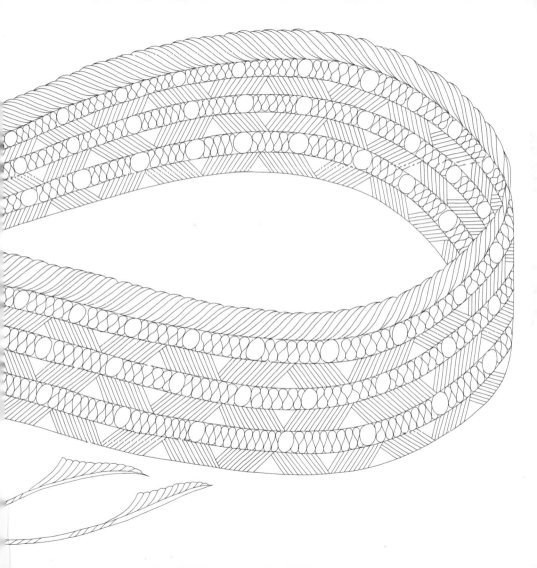

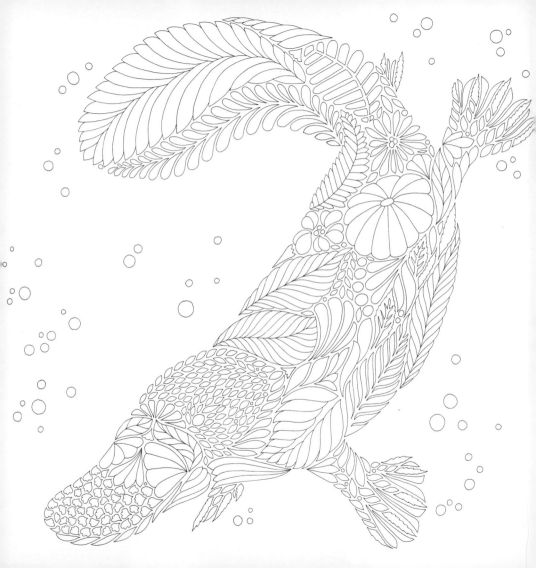

Curious Creatures

For those of you who are curious to know exactly what
creatures are featured, here's a list of the illustrations,
in the order that they appear in the book.

Flying fish
Coconut crab
Giant oarfish
Duck-billed platypus
Beaver
Narwhal
Plumed Basilisk lizard
Rajah Brooke's Birdwing butterfly
Poison dart frogs
Amazonian royal flycatcher
Praying mantis
Scalloped hammerhead shark
Northern gannet
Gerenuk
Mandarinfish and Dragon wrasse
Chinese water deer

Axolotl

Sealife:
Sea anemones;
Giant clam;
Sea sponge;
Christmas tree worms;
Coral

Bactrian camel
Fennec fox
Giant squid
Patagonian mara
King-of-Saxony bird-
of-paradise
Hummingbird hawk-moth
Devil lionfish
Manta ray
May bugs
Sailfish
Macaroni penguin
Malayan tapirs
Hermit crab
Peacock mantis shrimp
American white pelicans

Sea urchins
Mimic octopus
Chambered nautilus
Weedy sea dragons
Blue-footed booby
Elephant shrew
Okapi
Tufted puffin
Black-throated loons
Rhinoceros hornbill
Crested porcupine

Moths:
Rosy maple moth;
Chinese moon moth;
Luna moth;
Indonesian owl moth;
Poplar hawk-moth

Greater prairie chicken
Shoebill
Yeti crab
Pygmy seahorses
Jewel beetles
Longhorn cowfish

Pipefish
Kiwi
Mandarin duck
Lion's mane jellyfish
Walrus
Moose
Amazonian leaf-footed bugs

Caterpillars:
Giant Peacock moth caterpillar;
Joseph's Coat moth caterpillar;
Southern Marbled Emperor moth caterpillar

Great grey owl
Long-eared jerboa
Brown-throated sloths
Golden pheasant
Tibetan sand fox
Jackson's chameleon

Create your own curious creatures here...

Test your colour palette here…